nourish™
notebook

Other Books by Aliene Thompson

Nourish™ Notebook — binder starter kit

NOURISH™ BIBLE STUDY SERIES:

Dream Builder

Brave Heart

You Belong to the Bridegroom

PAPERBACK EDITION

nourish™ notebook

BIBLE STUDY JOURNAL

 Aliene Thompson

TREASURED
MINISTRIES

nourish™
BIBLE STUDY METHOD

Published by Nourish Resources
1105 Classic Road, Apex, NC 27539

ISBN 978-1-7337279-5-2 (paperback edition)

Editing and cover design by ChristianEditingServices.com
Cover image by hautestock.co
Interior design and typesetting by Beth Shagene

Printed in the United States of America.

TREASURED
MINISTRIES

info@treasuredministries.com
www.TreasuredMinistries.com

CONTENTS

*To get started on the 21-Day Challenge, visit:
www.TreasuredMinistries.com/21DayChallenge

Ready to begin your journey?

Let's do this!

Today's date: _____

This Nourish™ Notebook belongs to:

_____
Name

_____
Phone Number

_____
Address

_____
Email Address

Dear Treasured One,

I am so honored that you have chosen this resource and pray you will be blessed as you use it to dive into God's Word.

Creation of the *Nourish Notebook* flowed out of my own personal time with the Lord, my desire for a deeper, bolder prayer life, and my quest to develop the practice of renewing my mind to God's Word through biblical meditation. I wanted to find a way to pause from the hustle to hear God's voice helping me walk in truth, live an authentic faith-filled life, and become the woman God created me to be.

And so a three-year journey began to design the *Nourish Notebook*. Our team prayed. We invited other women into the process. We went back to the drawing board many times until it was time to let this butterfly out of the cocoon. And now that journey continues with you.

Welcome! Are you ready for the journey of a lifetime?

Before you begin using your *Nourish Notebook*, take the 21-Day Challenge. In 21 days, you will cultivate the life-changing habit of spending time in God's Word as you discover how to use the *Nourish Notebook*. I want this to be the best experience possible for you, which is why we've created the 21-Day Challenge so I can personally walk with you through this process step-by-step.

Let's take the next 21 days to water our dry, thirsty souls and find the nourishment we need to live every day with purpose—and to be equipped with truth for a lifetime.

To get started, visit www.TreasuredMinistries.com/21DayChallenge.

ONWARD!

Blessings,

Aliene Thompson

"Let Jesus turn your weeping
into something wonderful
as you seek him through his Word."

— *Aliene Thompson*

We believe . . .

Every woman matters and is valuable to God. Yet often life speaks a different story to our hearts, and we find it hard to believe God's truth about who we really are. Our compass to navigate life shifts away from our Creator and moves toward outside sources, slowly pulling us away from living the authentic faith-filled life God created us to live.

But Jesus invites us to live differently by seeing differently. This is the goal of the *Nourish™ Bible Study Method*. Walking by faith in his Word, written on our hearts through the Holy Spirit, we can discover the truth to right the tide and return to our authentic purpose.

One day at a time. One step of faith at a time.

This journey matters. *Your* journey matters because every woman is a part of God's amazing story.

> "'People do not live by bread alone,
> but by every word that comes
> from the mouth of God.'"
>
> — *Matthew 4:4*

Find time to nourish the soul

Jesus taught us in Matthew 4:4 that his revealed words are daily food, essential for nourishing our souls. Spending personal time with God to hear his Word for you is not merely an aspiring goal but also a necessary element for the health of your soul.

Yet every woman can relate to how life's demands drive us to care for the needs of others to the neglect of our own. This includes the frustration of trying to find time to tend to our soul God's way with personal time in his Word.

Without a plan in place, we might skip this daily nourishment and depend on our pastor's message on Sunday or grab a quick podcast or devotional instead. And while teachers of God's Word are an important part of the faith journey, they can never replace the personal daily nourishment needed for your soul.

By changing your approach, you *can* change this divine discipline from a daunting religious task to cross off your list to a delight for your soul that becomes a part of your daily rhythm of life.

"... the very words
I have spoken to you
are spirit and life."

— *John 6:63b*

Daily truth for victory

The *Nourish Notebook* provides a proven, effective, efficient weekly plan to cultivate the practice of connecting with Jesus through the study of his Word for a lifetime.

The 21-Day Challenge is your step-by-step guide to understand how to use your notebook so that you can develop a life-nourishing habit that you can carry with you through every step of your faith journey.

Your notebook, along with the 21-Day Challenge, will help you:

* Discover a way to develop a life-changing habit of connecting to God's Word.

* Uncover a clear and simple way to apply the *Nourish Bible Study Method* to any Bible passage, anytime.

* Nourish your soul so that you can live the life you were created for.

* Develop a bold prayer life that flows from your study of God's Word by using the prayer sheets within the *Nourish Notebook*.

* Incorporate the vital spiritual discipline of renewing your mind with God's truth and securing your thoughts in the right direction.

To get started, visit
www.TreasuredMinistries.com/21DayChallenge

HOW TO USE THE
NOURISH NOTEBOOK

1 WATCH DAY 1 OF THE 21-DAY CHALLENGE.

The first day of the 21-Day Challenge will dive deeper into how to use the *Nourish Notebook* as it helps you prepare your heart to receive refreshing words from God each day. To get started, visit www.TreasuredMinistries.com/21DayChallenge to sign up.

2 DISCOVER THE NOURISH™ BIBLE STUDY METHOD.

As you continue on your journey through the 21-Day Challenge, we will move one step at a time through the Nourish Bible Study Method. By the end of the 21 days, you have a practical method to putting the life-changing discipline of Bible meditation into your daily routine to change the way you live and think. You'll learn how to better connect with Jesus, so it is His voice you'll be able to discern as He guides you into the life you were created to live.

3 ALLOW GOD'S WORD TO NOURISH YOU TO LIVE DIFFERENTLY.

The *Nourish Notebook* is designed to be the key that helps you connect with the words of Jesus and encourages you to keep walking out your authentic, faith-filled purpose for the rest of your life. It's a way to pause on the word of God and let it wash over you, renewing your soul every day, so that you can live free and victoriously.

When you connect with Jesus, you naturally live differently, walk with confidence, and hear His voice as He guides you down the right path in your life.

LET'S DO THIS! Sign up for the 21-Day Challenge, start using your Nourish Notebook, and watch how God writes a new story on your heart as you start spending time in His Word by following the plan outlined for each day. Enjoy your journey.

We welcome your questions and are here to support you!

Let's stay connected.

Aliene Thompson

aliene@TreasuredMinistries.com

Facebook: facebook.com/Treasured.Ministries

Instagram: instagram.com/TreasuredMinistries

YouTube: Treasured Ministries

Podcast: Live Treasured

Website: TreasuredMinistries.com

About the Cover ...

During long summertime walks on the North Carolina seashore, as the textured taupe coastal sand pushes between my toes, my eyes search for sea glass to collect. What is sea glass? Shards of various shades of broken glass with jagged edges transformed over time into precious frosty, soft-edged treasures by the currents and waves of the ocean.

If you have read *You Belong to the Bridegroom*, you know why sea glass has a special place in my heart. In this study a woman shares her story to show that just as broken pieces of sea glass can be vessels of beauty, God takes the broken things of our lives and makes them beautiful.

I love this imagery and have become a collector of sea glass treasures tossed onto our North Carolina shores. Storms often dredge such treasures from the depths and cast them to the shore. Each piece of sea glass is a treasure, each one different. Each difficult journey becomes the very force that creates the beauty.

Sea glass inspired the cover of the Nourish Notebook. Every time you pick up your notebook, I pray you will remember that spending time in God's presence through the study of his Word will change your life.

Jesus takes the broken things in our lives and makes them beautiful.

21-DAY CHALLENGE

"'People do not live by bread alone,
but by every word that comes
from the mouth of God.'"

—Matthew 4:4

"*God's Word* is a *seed* that creates a *harvest* in our lives to *nourish* others."

—Aliene Thompson

21-DAY CHALLENGE NOTES

To sign up, visit: www.TreasuredMinistries.com/21DayChallenge

21-DAY CHALLENGE NOTES
(To sign up, visit www.TreasuredMinistries.com/21DayChallenge.)

Day 1

_____
_____
_____
_____
_____
_____
_____

Day 2

_____
_____
_____
_____
_____
_____
_____

Day 3

_____
_____
_____
_____
_____
_____
_____

21-DAY CHALLENGE NOTES

Day 4

_____

_____

_____

_____

_____

_____

_____

_____

Day 5

_____

_____

_____

_____

_____

_____

_____

_____

Day 6

_____

_____

_____

_____

_____

_____

_____

_____

21-DAY CHALLENGE NOTES

Day 7

_____

Day 8

_____

21-DAY CHALLENGE NOTES

Put it into practice . . .

Nourish Scripture: _Ephesians 1:1–11_

❤ **TAKE THE *REVEAL* STEP OF THE NOURISH™ BIBLE STUDY METHOD.**
Connect with Jesus by studying the Weekly Nourish Scripture* and allowing the Holy Spirit to reveal truth in those verses. Prayerfully read over and reflect on the passage. Mark any phrases, verses, or words that catch your attention. Journal and learn as the Lord leads you.

*Inside today's 21-Day Challenge video, I will share the Nourish Scripture. Moving forward, at the bottom of your Treasured Devotion, you will find a Nourish Scripture reference to study for the week.

21-DAY CHALLENGE NOTES

Day 9

_____

_____

_____

_____

_____

_____

_____

_____

_____

_____

Day 10

_____

_____

_____

_____

_____

_____

_____

_____

_____

_____

21-DAY CHALLENGE NOTES

Put it into practice . . .   Nourish Scripture: _Ephesians 1:1–11_

 TAKE THE *RESPOND* STEP OF THE NOURISH™ BIBLE STUDY METHOD.
Respond to activate truth in your life. The acronym **IMPACT**™ provides questions to help you apply the truth from your weekly Nourish Scripture. **Sometimes you may not have answers for all six questions.**

IMAGE OF GOD TO TRUST? An attribute of God, Jesus, or the Holy Spirit to trust.

MESSAGE TO SHARE? A word of encouragement, truth, or prayer to share.

PROMISE TO TREASURE? A promise in the Bible to believe.

ACTION TO TAKE? A specific step God is calling you to take.

CORE IDENTITY IN CHRIST TO AFFIRM? A truth about how God sees you to affirm.

TRANSGRESSION TO CONFESS? A sin to acknowledge for help, healing, and restoration through Christ.

21-DAY CHALLENGE NOTES

Day 11

Day 12

Put it into practice . . .   Nourish Scripture: _Ephesians 1:1–11_

 TAKE THE *RENEW* STEP OF THE NOURISH™ BIBLE STUDY METHOD.

Like an anchor that secures its vessel, biblical meditation secures truth to transform your life. Take five minutes to *renew* your mind by focusing on one word, verse, or truth that the Holy Spirit revealed through the Bible during your week of study. Record your truth below and on your Anchor of Truth card.* Quiet your thoughts. Focus on the truth. Read the truth. Pray the truth.

My anchor of truth

 RECORD AND REVIEW ATTRIBUTES OF GOD.

Write the attributes you discovered from yesterday's IMPACT question "An Image of God to Trust" in the GOD IS section on page 111.

 DEFINE AND DECLARE WHO YOU ARE IN CHRIST.

Reflect on your answers to yesterday's IMPACT question "A Core Identity in Christ to Affirm." Rewrite one answer as an "In Christ, I Am" statement in the AFFIRMATION section on page 97 and read aloud.

*Anchor of Truth Cards are available at www.TreasuredMinistries.com/shop.

21-DAY CHALLENGE NOTES

Day 13

21-DAY CHALLENGE NOTES

Day 14

_____

_____

_____

_____

_____

_____

_____

_____

_____

_____

_____

_____

_____

_____

_____

_____

_____

_____

_____

_____

_____

_____

Day 15-21 For Days 15-21, we will use the actual *Nourish Notes* pages in the next section. Turn to page 33 to continue with Day 15.

MY NOTES

MY NOTES

NOURISH™ NOTES

"... the very words I have spoken
to you are spirit and life."

—John 6:63b

"As *Jesus captures* our hearts
with his *words*,
we capture the *life* he created
for us to *live*."

—Aliene Thompson

DAY ONE > PREPARE

Today's Date: _____

1 **READ YOUR TREASURED DEVOTION.**

Prepare your heart by reading your Treasured Devotion. (To discover more, visit www.treasuredministries
.com/devotions.)

2 **LISTEN AND JOURNAL.**

Take a moment to listen to God and journal. You might write a prayer, a response to the devotion, or
something God has impressed on your heart.

On my heart this week . . .

3 **PREPARE YOUR WEEKLY PERSONAL PRAYER SHEET.**

Turn the page and follow the guidelines to set up a two-page Personal Prayer Sheet for the week.

4 **WRITE THE NOURISH SCRIPTURE REFERENCE ON EACH DAY OF STUDY.**

At the bottom of your Treasured Devotion, you will find a Nourish Scripture reference. Write this scripture
in the designated space at the top of your Nourish Notes pages for days two, three, and four.

WEEKLY PERSONAL PRAYER SHEET

worship > thanksgiving > ask

---

worship > TO BEGIN, CENTER YOUR FOCUS ON GOD.

MEDITATE ON GOD'S WORD: Using your Anchor of Truth Card from last week's Nourish Notes,* renew your mind on that truth. Quiet and focus your thoughts. Pray the truth. Say the truth. Meditate on God's truth.

CONTINUE BY WORSHIPING GOD FOR WHO HE IS: Each week choose three attributes from the GOD IS section of your notebook. Write your list below and continue your prayer time with worship.

1 _____   2 _____   3 _____

---

thanksgiving > AFTER WORSHIP, GIVE THANKS & CULTIVATE GRATITUDE.

CULTIVATE GRATITUDE: Daily record three blessings and give thanks to God.

Gratitude inventory

_____

_____

_____

_____

_____

_____

_____

_____

_____

_____

_____

_____

---

*Take the 21 Day Challenge to learn more about the Anchor of Truth Cards and Nourish Notes (www.TreasuredMinistries.com/21DayChallenge)

WEEKLY PERSONAL PRAYER SHEET

worship > thanksgiving > ask

ask > CONCLUDE BY ASKING GOD FOR WHAT YOU NEED.

PRAYER CIRCLES: Define three bold prayer requests and daily declare a circle of prayer around them.

PRAYER FROM NOURISH NOTES: Review your Nourish Notes from last week and record anything God revealed that you want to cover in prayer.

PRAYER FOR THE WEEK: Think through your week and record any prayer requests you want to remember. Update daily.

PRAYER FOR OTHERS: Intercession is praying for others. List people on your heart to lift up in prayer. Update as needed.

SUNDAY

MONDAY

TUESDAY

WEDNESDAY

THURSDAY

FRIDAY

SATURDAY

DAY TWO > REVEAL

Nourish Scripture: _____

PRAY.

Pray with purpose following the framework on your Weekly Personal Prayer Sheet.

2 TAKE THE *REVEAL* STEP OF THE NOURISH™ BIBLE STUDY METHOD.

Connect with Jesus by studying the Weekly Nourish Scripture and allowing the Holy Spirit to reveal truth in those verses. Prayerfully read over and reflect on the passage. Mark any phrases, verses, or words that catch your attention. Journal and learn as the Lord leads you.

3 AFFIRM YOUR IDENTITY IN CHRIST.

Conclude your quiet time by turning to the AFFIRMATION section on page 97 to read your "In Christ, I Am" statements aloud.

DAY THREE > RESPOND

Nourish Scripture: _____

1 PRAY.

Pray with purpose following the framework on your Weekly Personal Prayer Sheet.

2 TAKE THE *RESPOND* STEP OF THE NOURISH™ BIBLE STUDY METHOD.

Respond to activate truth in your life. The acronym **IMPACT**™ provides questions to help you apply the truth from your weekly Nourish Scripture. **Sometimes you may not have answers for all six questions.**

IMAGE OF GOD TO TRUST? An attribute of God, Jesus, or the Holy Spirit to trust.

MESSAGE TO SHARE? A word of encouragement, truth, or prayer to share.

PROMISE TO TREASURE? A promise in the Bible to believe.

ACTION TO TAKE? A specific step God is calling you to take.

CORE IDENTITY IN CHRIST TO AFFIRM? A truth about how God sees you to affirm.

TRANSGRESSION TO CONFESS? A sin to acknowledge for help, healing, and restoration through Christ.

3 AFFIRM YOUR IDENTITY IN CHRIST.

Conclude your quiet time by turning to the AFFIRMATION section on page 97 to read your "In Christ, I Am" statements aloud.

DAY FOUR > RENEW

Nourish Scripture: _____

 PRAY.

Pray with purpose following the framework on your Weekly Personal Prayer Sheet.

2 TAKE THE *RENEW* STEP OF THE NOURISH™ BIBLE STUDY METHOD.

Like an anchor that secures its vessel, biblical meditation secures truth to transform your life. Take five minutes to *renew* your mind by focusing on one word, verse, or truth that the Holy Spirit revealed through the Bible during your week of study. Record your truth below and on your Anchor of Truth card.* Quiet your thoughts. Focus on the truth. Read the truth. Pray the truth.

My anchor of truth

3 RECORD AND REVIEW ATTRIBUTES OF GOD.

Write the attributes you discovered from yesterday's IMPACT question "An Image of God to Trust" in the GOD IS section on page 111.

4 DEFINE AND DECLARE WHO YOU ARE IN CHRIST.

Reflect on your answers to yesterday's IMPACT question "A Core Identity in Christ to Affirm." Rewrite one answer as an "In Christ, I Am" statement in the AFFIRMATION section on page 97 and read aloud.

---

*Anchor of Truth Cards are available at www.TreasuredMinistries.com/shop.

DAY FIVE > CONNECT

1 **PRAY.**
Pray with purpose following the framework on your Weekly Personal Prayer Sheet.

2 **CONNECT AND SHARE TRUTH.**
Watch the weekly teaching message called the Treasured Tribe Talk and consider posting your thoughts online. To discover more, visit www.TreasuredMinistries.com/devotions.

MY NOTES

Rest and Reflect

The remaining days in your week provide time to rest, reflect, and catch up on any days of study you may have missed during the week. Use the space below however you decide. You could take notes from your small group time if applicable, write down additional thoughts from your week of study, record sermon notes, journal, list your goals and dreams, or just leave these pages blank. It's entirely up to you!

DAY ONE > PREPARE

Today's Date: _____

1 READ YOUR TREASURED DEVOTION.

Prepare your heart by reading your Treasured Devotion. (To discover more, visit www.treasuredministries
.com/devotions.)

2 LISTEN AND JOURNAL.

Take a moment to listen to God and journal. You might write a prayer, a response to the devotion, or
something God has impressed on your heart.

On my heart this week . . .

3 PREPARE YOUR WEEKLY PERSONAL PRAYER SHEET.

Turn the page and follow the guidelines to set up a two-page Personal Prayer Sheet for the week.

4 WRITE THE NOURISH SCRIPTURE REFERENCE ON EACH DAY OF STUDY.

At the bottom of your Treasured Devotion, you will find a Nourish Scripture reference. Write this scripture
in the designated space at the top of your Nourish Notes pages for days two, three, and four.

WEEKLY PERSONAL PRAYER SHEET

worship > thanksgiving > ask

---

worship > TO BEGIN, CENTER YOUR FOCUS ON GOD.

MEDITATE ON GOD'S WORD: Using your Anchor of Truth Card from last week's Nourish Notes, renew your mind on that truth. Quiet and focus your thoughts. Pray the truth. Say the truth. Meditate on God's truth.

CONTINUE BY WORSHIPING GOD FOR WHO HE IS: Each week choose three attributes from the GOD IS section of your notebook. Write your list below and continue your prayer time with worship.

1 _____ 2 _____ 3 _____

---

thanksgiving > AFTER WORSHIP, GIVE THANKS & CULTIVATE GRATITUDE.

CULTIVATE GRATITUDE: Daily record three blessings and give thanks to God.

Gratitude inventory

_____

_____

_____

_____

_____

_____

_____

_____

_____

_____

_____

_____

_____

_____

WEEKLY PERSONAL PRAYER SHEET

worship > thanksgiving > ask

---

ask > **CONCLUDE BY ASKING GOD FOR WHAT YOU NEED.**

PRAYER CIRCLES: Define three bold prayer requests and daily declare a circle of prayer around them.

PRAYER FROM NOURISH NOTES: Review your Nourish Notes from last week and record anything God revealed that you want to cover in prayer.

PRAYER FOR THE WEEK: Think through your week and record any prayer requests you want to remember. Update daily.

PRAYER FOR OTHERS: Intercession is praying for others. List people on your heart to lift up in prayer. Update as needed.

SUNDAY

MONDAY

TUESDAY

WEDNESDAY

THURSDAY

FRIDAY

SATURDAY

DAY TWO > REVEAL

Nourish Scripture: _____

 PRAY.

Pray with purpose following the framework on your Weekly Personal Prayer Sheet.

2 TAKE THE *REVEAL* STEP OF THE NOURISH™ BIBLE STUDY METHOD.

Connect with Jesus by studying the Weekly Nourish Scripture and allowing the Holy Spirit to reveal truth in those verses. Prayerfully read over and reflect on the passage. Mark any phrases, verses, or words that catch your attention. Journal and learn as the Lord leads you.

3 AFFIRM YOUR IDENTITY IN CHRIST.

Conclude your quiet time by turning to the AFFIRMATION section on page 97 to read your "In Christ, I Am" statements aloud.

DAY THREE > RESPOND

Nourish Scripture: _____

❶ PRAY.

Pray with purpose following the framework on your Weekly Personal Prayer Sheet.

❷ TAKE THE *RESPOND* STEP OF THE NOURISH™ BIBLE STUDY METHOD.

Respond to activate truth in your life. The acronym **IMPACT™** provides questions to help you apply the truth from your weekly Nourish Scripture. **Sometimes you may not have answers for all six questions.**

IMAGE OF GOD TO TRUST? An attribute of God, Jesus, or the Holy Spirit to trust.

MESSAGE TO SHARE? A word of encouragement, truth, or prayer to share.

PROMISE TO TREASURE? A promise in the Bible to believe.

ACTION TO TAKE? A specific step God is calling you to take.

CORE IDENTITY IN CHRIST TO AFFIRM? A truth about how God sees you to affirm.

TRANSGRESSION TO CONFESS? A sin to acknowledge for help, healing, and restoration through Christ.

❸ AFFIRM YOUR IDENTITY IN CHRIST.

Conclude your quiet time by turning to the AFFIRMATION section on page 97 to read your "In Christ, I Am" statements aloud.

DAY FOUR > RENEW

Nourish Scripture: _____

 PRAY.

Pray with purpose following the framework on your Weekly Personal Prayer Sheet.

2 TAKE THE *RENEW* STEP OF THE NOURISH™ BIBLE STUDY METHOD.

Like an anchor that secures its vessel, biblical meditation secures truth to transform your life. Take five minutes to *renew* your mind by focusing on one word, verse, or truth that the Holy Spirit revealed through the Bible during your week of study. Record your truth below and on your Anchor of Truth card. Quiet your thoughts. Focus on the truth. Read the truth. Pray the truth.

My anchor of truth

3 RECORD AND REVIEW ATTRIBUTES OF GOD.

Write the attributes you discovered from yesterday's IMPACT question "An Image of God to Trust" in the GOD IS section on page 111.

4 DEFINE AND DECLARE WHO YOU ARE IN CHRIST.

Reflect on your answers to yesterday's IMPACT question "A Core Identity in Christ to Affirm." Rewrite one answer as an "In Christ, I Am" statement in the AFFIRMATION section on page 97 and read aloud.

DAY FIVE > CONNECT

1 PRAY.

Pray with purpose following the framework on your Weekly Personal Prayer Sheet.

2 CONNECT AND SHARE TRUTH.

Watch the weekly teaching message called the Treasured Tribe Talk and consider posting your thoughts online. To discover more, visit www.TreasuredMinistries.com/devotions.

MY NOTES
Rest and Reflect

The remaining days in your week provide time to rest, reflect, and catch up on any days of study you may have missed during the week. Use the space below however you decide. You could take notes from your small group time if applicable, write down additional thoughts from your week of study, record sermon notes, journal, list your goals and dreams, or just leave these pages blank. It's entirely up to you!

DAY ONE > PREPARE

Today's Date: _____

1 READ YOUR TREASURED DEVOTION.

Prepare your heart by reading your Treasured Devotion. (To discover more, visit www.treasuredministries .com/devotions.)

2 LISTEN AND JOURNAL.

Take a moment to listen to God and journal. You might write a prayer, a response to the devotion, or something God has impressed on your heart.

On my heart this week . . .

3 PREPARE YOUR WEEKLY PERSONAL PRAYER SHEET.

Turn the page and follow the guidelines to set up a two-page Personal Prayer Sheet for the week.

4 WRITE THE NOURISH SCRIPTURE REFERENCE ON EACH DAY OF STUDY.

At the bottom of your Treasured Devotion, you will find a Nourish Scripture reference. Write this scripture in the designated space at the top of your Nourish Notes pages for days two, three, and four.

WEEKLY PERSONAL PRAYER SHEET

worship > thanksgiving > ask

---

worship > TO BEGIN, CENTER YOUR FOCUS ON GOD.

MEDITATE ON GOD'S WORD: Using your Anchor of Truth Card from last week's Nourish Notes, renew your mind on that truth. Quiet and focus your thoughts. Pray the truth. Say the truth. Meditate on God's truth.

CONTINUE BY WORSHIPING GOD FOR WHO HE IS: Each week choose three attributes from the GOD IS section of your notebook. Write your list below and continue your prayer time with worship.

1 _____ 2 _____ 3 _____

---

thanksgiving > AFTER WORSHIP, GIVE THANKS & CULTIVATE GRATITUDE.

CULTIVATE GRATITUDE: Daily record three blessings and give thanks to God.

Gratitude inventory

_____

_____

_____

_____

_____

_____

_____

_____

_____

_____

_____

_____

_____

_____

_____

_____

WEEKLY PERSONAL PRAYER SHEET

worship > thanksgiving > ask

---

ask > CONCLUDE BY ASKING GOD FOR WHAT YOU NEED.

PRAYER CIRCLES: Define three bold prayer requests and daily declare a circle of prayer around them.

PRAYER FROM NOURISH NOTES: Review your Nourish Notes from last week and record anything God revealed that you want to cover in prayer.

PRAYER FOR THE WEEK: Think through your week and record any prayer requests you want to remember. Update daily.

PRAYER FOR OTHERS: Intercession is praying for others. List people on your heart to lift up in prayer. Update as needed.

SUNDAY

MONDAY

TUESDAY

WEDNESDAY

THURSDAY

FRIDAY

SATURDAY

DAY TWO > REVEAL

Nourish Scripture: _____

1 PRAY.

Pray with purpose following the framework on your Weekly Personal Prayer Sheet.

2 TAKE THE *REVEAL* STEP OF THE NOURISH™ BIBLE STUDY METHOD.

Connect with Jesus by studying the Weekly Nourish Scripture and allowing the Holy Spirit to reveal truth in those verses. Prayerfully read over and reflect on the passage. Mark any phrases, verses, or words that catch your attention. Journal and learn as the Lord leads you.

3 AFFIRM YOUR IDENTITY IN CHRIST.

Conclude your quiet time by turning to the AFFIRMATION section on page 97 to read your "In Christ, I Am" statements aloud.

DAY THREE > RESPOND

Nourish Scripture: _____

1 PRAY.
Pray with purpose following the framework on your Weekly Personal Prayer Sheet.

2 TAKE THE *RESPOND* STEP OF THE NOURISH™ BIBLE STUDY METHOD.
Respond to activate truth in your life. The acronym **IMPACT**™ provides questions to help you apply the truth from your weekly Nourish Scripture. **Sometimes you may not have answers for all six questions.**

IMAGE OF GOD TO TRUST? An attribute of God, Jesus, or the Holy Spirit to trust.

MESSAGE TO SHARE? A word of encouragement, truth, or prayer to share.

PROMISE TO TREASURE? A promise in the Bible to believe.

ACTION TO TAKE? A specific step God is calling you to take.

CORE IDENTITY IN CHRIST TO AFFIRM? A truth about how God sees you to affirm.

TRANSGRESSION TO CONFESS? A sin to acknowledge for help, healing, and restoration through Christ.

3 AFFIRM YOUR IDENTITY IN CHRIST.
Conclude your quiet time by turning to the AFFIRMATION section on page 97 to read your "In Christ, I Am" statements aloud.

DAY FOUR > RENEW

Nourish Scripture: _____

 PRAY.

Pray with purpose following the framework on your Weekly Personal Prayer Sheet.

② TAKE THE *RENEW* STEP OF THE NOURISH™ BIBLE STUDY METHOD.

Like an anchor that secures its vessel, biblical meditation secures truth to transform your life. Take five minutes to *renew* your mind by focusing on one word, verse, or truth that the Holy Spirit revealed through the Bible during your week of study. Record your truth below and on your Anchor of Truth card. Quiet your thoughts. Focus on the truth. Read the truth. Pray the truth.

My anchor of truth

③ RECORD AND REVIEW ATTRIBUTES OF GOD.

Write the attributes you discovered from yesterday's IMPACT question "An Image of God to Trust" in the GOD IS section on page 111.

④ DEFINE AND DECLARE WHO YOU ARE IN CHRIST.

Reflect on your answers to yesterday's IMPACT question "A Core Identity in Christ to Affirm." Rewrite one answer as an "In Christ, I Am" statement in the AFFIRMATION section on page 97 and read aloud.

DAY FIVE > CONNECT

1 PRAY.

Pray with purpose following the framework on your Weekly Personal Prayer Sheet.

2 CONNECT AND SHARE TRUTH.

Watch the weekly teaching message called the Treasured Tribe Talk and consider posting your thoughts online. To discover more, visit www.TreasuredMinistries.com/devotions.

MY NOTES
Rest and Reflect

The remaining days in your week provide time to rest, reflect, and catch up on any days of study you may have missed during the week. Use the space below however you decide. You could take notes from your small group time if applicable, write down additional thoughts from your week of study, record sermon notes, journal, list your goals and dreams, or just leave these pages blank. It's entirely up to you!

DAY ONE > PREPARE

Today's Date: _____

❶ READ YOUR TREASURED DEVOTION.

Prepare your heart by reading your Treasured Devotion. (To discover more, visit www.treasuredministries .com/devotions.)

❷ LISTEN AND JOURNAL.

Take a moment to listen to God and journal. You might write a prayer, a response to the devotion, or something God has impressed on your heart.

On my heart this week . . .

❸ PREPARE YOUR WEEKLY PERSONAL PRAYER SHEET.

Turn the page and follow the guidelines to set up a two-page Personal Prayer Sheet for the week.

❹ WRITE THE NOURISH SCRIPTURE REFERENCE ON EACH DAY OF STUDY.

At the bottom of your Treasured Devotion, you will find a Nourish Scripture reference. Write this scripture in the designated space at the top of your Nourish Notes pages for days two, three, and four.

WEEKLY PERSONAL PRAYER SHEET

worship > thanksgiving > ask

---

worship > TO BEGIN, CENTER YOUR FOCUS ON GOD.

MEDITATE ON GOD'S WORD: Using your Anchor of Truth Card from last week's Nourish Notes, renew your mind on that truth. Quiet and focus your thoughts. Pray the truth. Say the truth. Meditate on God's truth.

CONTINUE BY WORSHIPING GOD FOR WHO HE IS: Each week choose three attributes from the GOD IS section of your notebook. Write your list below and continue your prayer time with worship.

1 _____ 2 _____ 3 _____

---

thanksgiving > AFTER WORSHIP, GIVE THANKS & CULTIVATE GRATITUDE.

CULTIVATE GRATITUDE: Daily record three blessings and give thanks to God.

Gratitude inventory

_____

_____

_____

_____

_____

_____

_____

_____

_____

_____

_____

WEEKLY PERSONAL PRAYER SHEET

worship > thanksgiving > ask

---

ask > CONCLUDE BY ASKING GOD FOR WHAT YOU NEED.

PRAYER CIRCLES: Define three bold prayer requests and daily declare a circle of prayer around them.

PRAYER FROM NOURISH NOTES: Review your Nourish Notes from last week and record anything God revealed that you want to cover in prayer.

PRAYER FOR THE WEEK: Think through your week and record any prayer requests you want to remember. Update daily.

PRAYER FOR OTHERS: Intercession is praying for others. List people on your heart to lift up in prayer. Update as needed.

SUNDAY

MONDAY

TUESDAY

WEDNESDAY

THURSDAY

FRIDAY

SATURDAY

DAY TWO > REVEAL

Nourish Scripture: _____

1 PRAY.

Pray with purpose following the framework on your Weekly Personal Prayer Sheet.

2 TAKE THE *REVEAL* STEP OF THE NOURISH™ BIBLE STUDY METHOD.

Connect with Jesus by studying the Weekly Nourish Scripture and allowing the Holy Spirit to reveal truth in those verses. Prayerfully read over and reflect on the passage. Mark any phrases, verses, or words that catch your attention. Journal and learn as the Lord leads you.

3 AFFIRM YOUR IDENTITY IN CHRIST.

Conclude your quiet time by turning to the AFFIRMATION section on page 97 to read your "In Christ, I Am" statements aloud.

DAY THREE > RESPOND

Nourish Scripture: _____

1 PRAY.
Pray with purpose following the framework on your Weekly Personal Prayer Sheet.

2 TAKE THE *RESPOND* STEP OF THE NOURISH™ BIBLE STUDY METHOD.
Respond to activate truth in your life. The acronym **IMPACT™** provides questions to help you apply the truth from your weekly Nourish Scripture. **Sometimes you may not have answers for all six questions.**

IMAGE OF GOD TO TRUST? An attribute of God, Jesus, or the Holy Spirit to trust.

MESSAGE TO SHARE? A word of encouragement, truth, or prayer to share.

PROMISE TO TREASURE? A promise in the Bible to believe.

ACTION TO TAKE? A specific step God is calling you to take.

CORE IDENTITY IN CHRIST TO AFFIRM? A truth about how God sees you to affirm.

TRANSGRESSION TO CONFESS? A sin to acknowledge for help, healing, and restoration through Christ.

3 AFFIRM YOUR IDENTITY IN CHRIST.
Conclude your quiet time by turning to the AFFIRMATION section on page 97 to read your "In Christ, I Am" statements aloud.

DAY FOUR > RENEW

Nourish Scripture: _____

1 PRAY.
Pray with purpose following the framework on your Weekly Personal Prayer Sheet.

2 TAKE THE *RENEW* STEP OF THE NOURISH™ BIBLE STUDY METHOD.
Like an anchor that secures its vessel, biblical meditation secures truth to transform your life. Take five minutes to *renew* your mind by focusing on one word, verse, or truth that the Holy Spirit revealed through the Bible during your week of study. Record your truth below and on your Anchor of Truth card. Quiet your thoughts. Focus on the truth. Read the truth. Pray the truth.

My anchor of truth

3 RECORD AND REVIEW ATTRIBUTES OF GOD.
Write the attributes you discovered from yesterday's IMPACT question "An Image of God to Trust" in the GOD IS section on page 111.

4 DEFINE AND DECLARE WHO YOU ARE IN CHRIST.
Reflect on your answers to yesterday's IMPACT question "A Core Identity in Christ to Affirm." Rewrite one answer as an "In Christ, I Am" statement in the AFFIRMATION section on page 97 and read aloud.

DAY FIVE > CONNECT

1 PRAY.

Pray with purpose following the framework on your Weekly Personal Prayer Sheet.

2 CONNECT AND SHARE TRUTH.

Watch the weekly teaching message called the Treasured Tribe Talk and consider posting your thoughts online. To discover more, visit www.TreasuredMinistries.com/devotions.

MY NOTES

Rest and Reflect

The remaining days in your week provide time to rest, reflect, and catch up on any days of study you may have missed during the week. Use the space below however you decide. You could take notes from your small group time if applicable, write down additional thoughts from your week of study, record sermon notes, journal, list your goals and dreams, or just leave these pages blank. It's entirely up to you!

DAY ONE > PREPARE

Today's Date: _____

❶ READ YOUR TREASURED DEVOTION.

Prepare your heart by reading your Treasured Devotion. (To discover more, visit www.treasuredministries .com/devotions.)

❷ LISTEN AND JOURNAL.

Take a moment to listen to God and journal. You might write a prayer, a response to the devotion, or something God has impressed on your heart.

On my heart this week . . .

❸ PREPARE YOUR WEEKLY PERSONAL PRAYER SHEET.

Turn the page and follow the guidelines to set up a two-page Personal Prayer Sheet for the week.

❹ WRITE THE NOURISH SCRIPTURE REFERENCE ON EACH DAY OF STUDY.

At the bottom of your Treasured Devotion, you will find a Nourish Scripture reference. Write this scripture in the designated space at the top of your Nourish Notes pages for days two, three, and four.

WEEKLY PERSONAL PRAYER SHEET

worship > thanksgiving > ask

---

worship > TO BEGIN, CENTER YOUR FOCUS ON GOD.

MEDITATE ON GOD'S WORD: Using your Anchor of Truth Card from last week's Nourish Notes, renew your mind on that truth. Quiet and focus your thoughts. Pray the truth. Say the truth. Meditate on God's truth.

CONTINUE BY WORSHIPING GOD FOR WHO HE IS: Each week choose three attributes from the GOD IS section of your notebook. Write your list below and continue your prayer time with worship.

1 _____ 2 _____ 3 _____

---

thanksgiving > AFTER WORSHIP, GIVE THANKS & CULTIVATE GRATITUDE.

CULTIVATE GRATITUDE: Daily record three blessings and give thanks to God.

Gratitude inventory

_____

_____

_____

_____

_____

_____

_____

_____

_____

_____

_____

_____

_____

WEEKLY PERSONAL PRAYER SHEET

worship > thanksgiving > ask

---

ask > CONCLUDE BY ASKING GOD FOR WHAT YOU NEED.

PRAYER CIRCLES: Define three bold prayer requests and daily declare a circle of prayer around them.

PRAYER FROM NOURISH NOTES: Review your Nourish Notes from last week and record anything God revealed that you want to cover in prayer.

PRAYER FOR THE WEEK: Think through your week and record any prayer requests you want to remember. Update daily.

PRAYER FOR OTHERS: Intercession is praying for others. List people on your heart to lift up in prayer. Update as needed.

SUNDAY

MONDAY

TUESDAY

WEDNESDAY

THURSDAY

FRIDAY

SATURDAY

DAY TWO > REVEAL

Nourish Scripture: _____

 PRAY.

Pray with purpose following the framework on your Weekly Personal Prayer Sheet.

2 TAKE THE *REVEAL* STEP OF THE NOURISH™ BIBLE STUDY METHOD.

Connect with Jesus by studying the Weekly Nourish Scripture and allowing the Holy Spirit to reveal truth in those verses. Prayerfully read over and reflect on the passage. Mark any phrases, verses, or words that catch your attention. Journal and learn as the Lord leads you.

3 AFFIRM YOUR IDENTITY IN CHRIST.

Conclude your quiet time by turning to the AFFIRMATION section on page 97 to read your "In Christ, I Am" statements aloud.

DAY THREE > RESPOND

Nourish Scripture: _____

❶ PRAY.
Pray with purpose following the framework on your Weekly Personal Prayer Sheet.

❷ TAKE THE *RESPOND* STEP OF THE NOURISH™ BIBLE STUDY METHOD.
Respond to activate truth in your life. The acronym **IMPACT™** provides questions to help you apply the truth from your weekly Nourish Scripture. **Sometimes you may not have answers for all six questions.**

IMAGE OF GOD TO TRUST? An attribute of God, Jesus, or the Holy Spirit to trust.

MESSAGE TO SHARE? A word of encouragement, truth, or prayer to share.

PROMISE TO TREASURE? A promise in the Bible to believe.

ACTION TO TAKE? A specific step God is calling you to take.

CORE IDENTITY IN CHRIST TO AFFIRM? A truth about how God sees you to affirm.

TRANSGRESSION TO CONFESS? A sin to acknowledge for help, healing, and restoration through Christ.

❸ AFFIRM YOUR IDENTITY IN CHRIST.
Conclude your quiet time by turning to the AFFIRMATION section on page 97 to read your "In Christ, I Am" statements aloud.

DAY FOUR > RENEW

Nourish Scripture: _____

 PRAY.

Pray with purpose following the framework on your Weekly Personal Prayer Sheet.

2 TAKE THE *RENEW* STEP OF THE NOURISH™ BIBLE STUDY METHOD.

Like an anchor that secures its vessel, biblical meditation secures truth to transform your life. Take five minutes to *renew* your mind by focusing on one word, verse, or truth that the Holy Spirit revealed through the Bible during your week of study. Record your truth below and on your Anchor of Truth card. Quiet your thoughts. Focus on the truth. Read the truth. Pray the truth.

My anchor of truth

3 RECORD AND REVIEW ATTRIBUTES OF GOD.

Write the attributes you discovered from yesterday's IMPACT question "An Image of God to Trust" in the GOD IS section on page 111.

4 DEFINE AND DECLARE WHO YOU ARE IN CHRIST.

Reflect on your answers to yesterday's IMPACT question "A Core Identity in Christ to Affirm." Rewrite one answer as an "In Christ, I Am" statement in the AFFIRMATION section on page 97 and read aloud.

DAY FIVE > CONNECT

1 PRAY.

Pray with purpose following the framework on your Weekly Personal Prayer Sheet.

2 CONNECT AND SHARE TRUTH.

Watch the weekly teaching message called the Treasured Tribe Talk and consider posting your thoughts online. To discover more, visit www.TreasuredMinistries.com/devotions.

MY NOTES
Rest and Reflect

The remaining days in your week provide time to rest, reflect, and catch up on any days of study you may have missed during the week. Use the space below however you decide. You could take notes from your small group time if applicable, write down additional thoughts from your week of study, record sermon notes, journal, list your goals and dreams, or just leave these pages blank. It's entirely up to you!

DAY ONE > PREPARE

Today's Date: _____

1 **READ YOUR TREASURED DEVOTION.**
Prepare your heart by reading your Treasured Devotion. (To discover more, visit www.treasuredministries
.com/devotions.)

2 **LISTEN AND JOURNAL.**
Take a moment to listen to God and journal. You might write a prayer, a response to the devotion, or
something God has impressed on your heart.

On my heart this week . . .

 3 **PREPARE YOUR WEEKLY PERSONAL PRAYER SHEET.**
Turn the page and follow the guidelines to set up a two-page Personal Prayer Sheet for the week.

 4 **WRITE THE NOURISH SCRIPTURE REFERENCE ON EACH DAY OF STUDY.**
At the bottom of your Treasured Devotion, you will find a Nourish Scripture reference. Write this scripture
in the designated space at the top of your Nourish Notes pages for days two, three, and four.

WEEKLY PERSONAL PRAYER SHEET

worship > thanksgiving > ask

---

worship > TO BEGIN, CENTER YOUR FOCUS ON GOD.

MEDITATE ON GOD'S WORD: Using your Anchor of Truth Card from last week's Nourish Notes, renew your mind on that truth. Quiet and focus your thoughts. Pray the truth. Say the truth. Meditate on God's truth.

CONTINUE BY WORSHIPING GOD FOR WHO HE IS: Each week choose three attributes from the GOD IS section of your notebook. Write your list below and continue your prayer time with worship.

1 _____   2 _____   3 _____

thanksgiving > AFTER WORSHIP, GIVE THANKS & CULTIVATE GRATITUDE.

CULTIVATE GRATITUDE: Daily record three blessings and give thanks to God.

Gratitude inventory

_____

_____

_____

_____

_____

_____

_____

_____

_____

_____

_____

_____

_____

_____

WEEKLY PERSONAL PRAYER SHEET

worship > thanksgiving > ask

ask > CONCLUDE BY ASKING GOD FOR WHAT YOU NEED.

PRAYER CIRCLES: Define three bold prayer requests and daily declare a circle of prayer around them.

PRAYER FROM NOURISH NOTES: Review your Nourish Notes from last week and record anything God revealed that you want to cover in prayer.

PRAYER FOR THE WEEK: Think through your week and record any prayer requests you want to remember. Update daily.

PRAYER FOR OTHERS: Intercession is praying for others. List people on your heart to lift up in prayer. Update as needed.

SUNDAY

MONDAY

TUESDAY

WEDNESDAY

THURSDAY

FRIDAY

SATURDAY

DAY TWO > REVEAL

Nourish Scripture: _____

 PRAY.

Pray with purpose following the framework on your Weekly Personal Prayer Sheet.

2 TAKE THE *REVEAL* STEP OF THE NOURISH™ BIBLE STUDY METHOD.

Connect with Jesus by studying the Weekly Nourish Scripture and allowing the Holy Spirit to reveal truth in those verses. Prayerfully read over and reflect on the passage. Mark any phrases, verses, or words that catch your attention. Journal and learn as the Lord leads you.

3 AFFIRM YOUR IDENTITY IN CHRIST.

Conclude your quiet time by turning to the AFFIRMATION section on page 97 to read your "In Christ, I Am" statements aloud.

DAY THREE > RESPOND

Nourish Scripture: _____

1 PRAY.
Pray with purpose following the framework on your Weekly Personal Prayer Sheet.

2 TAKE THE *RESPOND* STEP OF THE NOURISH™ BIBLE STUDY METHOD.
Respond to activate truth in your life. The acronym **IMPACT**™ provides questions to help you apply the truth from your weekly Nourish Scripture. **Sometimes you may not have answers for all six questions.**

IMAGE OF GOD TO TRUST? An attribute of God, Jesus, or the Holy Spirit to trust.

MESSAGE TO SHARE? A word of encouragement, truth, or prayer to share.

PROMISE TO TREASURE? A promise in the Bible to believe.

ACTION TO TAKE? A specific step God is calling you to take.

CORE IDENTITY IN CHRIST TO AFFIRM? A truth about how God sees you to affirm.

TRANSGRESSION TO CONFESS? A sin to acknowledge for help, healing, and restoration through Christ.

3 AFFIRM YOUR IDENTITY IN CHRIST.
Conclude your quiet time by turning to the AFFIRMATION section on page 97 to read your "In Christ, I Am" statements aloud.

DAY FOUR > RENEW

Nourish Scripture: _____

1 PRAY.

Pray with purpose following the framework on your Weekly Personal Prayer Sheet.

2 TAKE THE *RENEW* STEP OF THE NOURISH™ BIBLE STUDY METHOD.

Like an anchor that secures its vessel, biblical meditation secures truth to transform your life. Take five minutes to *renew* your mind by focusing on one word, verse, or truth that the Holy Spirit revealed through the Bible during your week of study. Record your truth below and on your Anchor of Truth card. Quiet your thoughts. Focus on the truth. Read the truth. Pray the truth.

My anchor of truth

3 RECORD AND REVIEW ATTRIBUTES OF GOD.

Write the attributes you discovered from yesterday's IMPACT question "An Image of God to Trust" in the GOD IS section on page 111.

4 DEFINE AND DECLARE WHO YOU ARE IN CHRIST.

Reflect on your answers to yesterday's IMPACT question "A Core Identity in Christ to Affirm." Rewrite one answer as an "In Christ, I Am" statement in the AFFIRMATION section on page 97 and read aloud.

DAY FIVE > CONNECT

1 PRAY.

Pray with purpose following the framework on your Weekly Personal Prayer Sheet.

2 CONNECT AND SHARE TRUTH.

Watch the weekly teaching message called the Treasured Tribe Talk and consider posting your thoughts online. To discover more, visit www.TreasuredMinistries.com/devotions.

MY NOTES

Rest and Reflect

The remaining days in your week provide time to rest, reflect, and catch up on any days of study you may have missed during the week. Use the space below however you decide. You could take notes from your small group time if applicable, write down additional thoughts from your week of study, record sermon notes, journal, list your goals and dreams, or just leave these pages blank. It's entirely up to you!

DAY ONE > PREPARE

Today's Date: _____

1 READ YOUR TREASURED DEVOTION.

Prepare your heart by reading your Treasured Devotion. (To discover more, visit www.treasuredministries .com/devotions.)

2 LISTEN AND JOURNAL.

Take a moment to listen to God and journal. You might write a prayer, a response to the devotion, or something God has impressed on your heart.

On my heart this week . . .

3 PREPARE YOUR WEEKLY PERSONAL PRAYER SHEET.

Turn the page and follow the guidelines to set up a two-page Personal Prayer Sheet for the week.

4 WRITE THE NOURISH SCRIPTURE REFERENCE ON EACH DAY OF STUDY.

At the bottom of your Treasured Devotion, you will find a Nourish Scripture reference. Write this scripture in the designated space at the top of your Nourish Notes pages for days two, three, and four.

WEEKLY PERSONAL PRAYER SHEET

worship > thanksgiving > ask

---

worship > TO BEGIN, CENTER YOUR FOCUS ON GOD.

MEDITATE ON GOD'S WORD: Using your Anchor of Truth Card from last week's Nourish Notes, renew your mind on that truth. Quiet and focus your thoughts. Pray the truth. Say the truth. Meditate on God's truth.

CONTINUE BY WORSHIPING GOD FOR WHO HE IS: Each week choose three attributes from the GOD IS section of your notebook. Write your list below and continue your prayer time with worship.

1 _____   2 _____   3 _____

---

thanksgiving > AFTER WORSHIP, GIVE THANKS & CULTIVATE GRATITUDE.

CULTIVATE GRATITUDE: Daily record three blessings and give thanks to God.

Gratitude inventory

_____

_____

_____

_____

_____

_____

_____

_____

_____

_____

_____

_____

_____

_____

_____

WEEKLY PERSONAL PRAYER SHEET

worship > thanksgiving > ask

ask > CONCLUDE BY ASKING GOD FOR WHAT YOU NEED.

PRAYER CIRCLES: Define three bold prayer requests and daily declare a circle of prayer around them.

PRAYER FROM NOURISH NOTES: Review your Nourish Notes from last week and record anything God revealed that you want to cover in prayer.

PRAYER FOR THE WEEK: Think through your week and record any prayer requests you want to remember. Update daily.

PRAYER FOR OTHERS: Intercession is praying for others. List people on your heart to lift up in prayer. Update as needed.

SUNDAY

MONDAY

TUESDAY

WEDNESDAY

THURSDAY

FRIDAY

SATURDAY

DAY TWO > REVEAL

Nourish Scripture: _____
_____

 PRAY.

Pray with purpose following the framework on your Weekly Personal Prayer Sheet.

2 **TAKE THE *REVEAL* STEP OF THE NOURISH™ BIBLE STUDY METHOD.**

Connect with Jesus by studying the Weekly Nourish Scripture and allowing the Holy Spirit to reveal truth in those verses. Prayerfully read over and reflect on the passage. Mark any phrases, verses, or words that catch your attention. Journal and learn as the Lord leads you.

 **AFFIRM YOUR IDENTITY IN CHRIST.**

Conclude your quiet time by turning to the AFFIRMATION section on page 97 to read your "In Christ, I Am" statements aloud.

DAY THREE > RESPOND

Nourish Scripture: _____

1 PRAY.
Pray with purpose following the framework on your Weekly Personal Prayer Sheet.

2 TAKE THE *RESPOND* STEP OF THE NOURISH™ BIBLE STUDY METHOD.
Respond to activate truth in your life. The acronym **IMPACT**™ provides questions to help you apply the truth from your weekly Nourish Scripture. **Sometimes you may not have answers for all six questions.**

IMAGE OF GOD TO TRUST? An attribute of God, Jesus, or the Holy Spirit to trust.

MESSAGE TO SHARE? A word of encouragement, truth, or prayer to share.

PROMISE TO TREASURE? A promise in the Bible to believe.

ACTION TO TAKE? A specific step God is calling you to take.

CORE IDENTITY IN CHRIST TO AFFIRM? A truth about how God sees you to affirm.

TRANSGRESSION TO CONFESS? A sin to acknowledge for help, healing, and restoration through Christ.

3 AFFIRM YOUR IDENTITY IN CHRIST.
Conclude your quiet time by turning to the AFFIRMATION section on page 97 to read your "In Christ, I Am" statements aloud.

DAY FOUR > RENEW

Nourish Scripture: _____

❶ PRAY.

Pray with purpose following the framework on your Weekly Personal Prayer Sheet.

---

❷ TAKE THE *RENEW* STEP OF THE NOURISH™ BIBLE STUDY METHOD.

Like an anchor that secures its vessel, biblical meditation secures truth to transform your life. Take five minutes to *renew* your mind by focusing on one word, verse, or truth that the Holy Spirit revealed through the Bible during your week of study. Record your truth below and on your Anchor of Truth card. Quiet your thoughts. Focus on the truth. Read the truth. Pray the truth.

My anchor of truth

---

❸ RECORD AND REVIEW ATTRIBUTES OF GOD.

Write the attributes you discovered from yesterday's IMPACT question "An Image of God to Trust" in the GOD IS section on page 111.

---

❹ DEFINE AND DECLARE WHO YOU ARE IN CHRIST.

Reflect on your answers to yesterday's IMPACT question "A Core Identity in Christ to Affirm." Rewrite one answer as an "In Christ, I Am" statement in the AFFIRMATION section on page 97 and read aloud.

DAY FIVE > CONNECT

1 PRAY.

Pray with purpose following the framework on your Weekly Personal Prayer Sheet.

2 CONNECT AND SHARE TRUTH.

Watch the weekly teaching message called the Treasured Tribe Talk and consider posting your thoughts online. To discover more, visit www.TreasuredMinistries.com/devotions.

MY NOTES
Rest and Reflect

The remaining days in your week provide time to rest, reflect, and catch up on any days of study you may have missed during the week. Use the space below however you decide. You could take notes from your small group time if applicable, write down additional thoughts from your week of study, record sermon notes, journal, list your goals and dreams, or just leave these pages blank. It's entirely up to you!

DAY ONE > PREPARE

Today's Date: _____

❶ READ YOUR TREASURED DEVOTION.

Prepare your heart by reading your Treasured Devotion. (To discover more, visit www.treasuredministries
.com/devotions.)

❷ LISTEN AND JOURNAL.

Take a moment to listen to God and journal. You might write a prayer, a response to the devotion, or
something God has impressed on your heart.

On my heart this week . . .

❸ PREPARE YOUR WEEKLY PERSONAL PRAYER SHEET.

Turn the page and follow the guidelines to set up a two-page Personal Prayer Sheet for the week.

❹ WRITE THE NOURISH SCRIPTURE REFERENCE ON EACH DAY OF STUDY.

At the bottom of your Treasured Devotion, you will find a Nourish Scripture reference. Write this scripture
in the designated space at the top of your Nourish Notes pages for days two, three, and four.

WEEKLY PERSONAL PRAYER SHEET

worship > thanksgiving > ask

---

worship > TO BEGIN, CENTER YOUR FOCUS ON GOD.

MEDITATE ON GOD'S WORD: Using your Anchor of Truth Card from last week's Nourish Notes, renew your mind on that truth. Quiet and focus your thoughts. Pray the truth. Say the truth. Meditate on God's truth.

CONTINUE BY WORSHIPING GOD FOR WHO HE IS: Each week choose three attributes from the GOD IS section of your notebook. Write your list below and continue your prayer time with worship.

1 _____ 2 _____ 3 _____

---

thanksgiving > AFTER WORSHIP, GIVE THANKS & CULTIVATE GRATITUDE.

CULTIVATE GRATITUDE: Daily record three blessings and give thanks to God.

Gratitude inventory

_____

_____

_____

_____

_____

_____

_____

_____

_____

_____

_____

_____

_____

WEEKLY PERSONAL PRAYER SHEET

worship > thanksgiving > ask

ask > CONCLUDE BY ASKING GOD FOR WHAT YOU NEED.

PRAYER CIRCLES: Define three bold prayer requests and daily declare a circle of prayer around them.

PRAYER FROM NOURISH NOTES: Review your Nourish Notes from last week and record anything God revealed that you want to cover in prayer.

PRAYER FOR THE WEEK: Think through your week and record any prayer requests you want to remember. Update daily.

PRAYER FOR OTHERS: Intercession is praying for others. List people on your heart to lift up in prayer. Update as needed.

SUNDAY

MONDAY

TUESDAY

WEDNESDAY

THURSDAY

FRIDAY

SATURDAY

DAY TWO > REVEAL

Nourish Scripture: _____

❶ PRAY.

Pray with purpose following the framework on your Weekly Personal Prayer Sheet.

❷ TAKE THE *REVEAL* STEP OF THE NOURISH™ BIBLE STUDY METHOD.

Connect with Jesus by studying the Weekly Nourish Scripture and allowing the Holy Spirit to reveal truth in those verses. Prayerfully read over and reflect on the passage. Mark any phrases, verses, or words that catch your attention. Journal and learn as the Lord leads you.

❸ AFFIRM YOUR IDENTITY IN CHRIST.

Conclude your quiet time by turning to the AFFIRMATION section on page 97 to read your "In Christ, I Am" statements aloud.

DAY THREE > RESPOND

Nourish Scripture: _____

1 PRAY.

Pray with purpose following the framework on your Weekly Personal Prayer Sheet.

2 TAKE THE *RESPOND* STEP OF THE NOURISH™ BIBLE STUDY METHOD.

Respond to activate truth in your life. The acronym **IMPACT**™ provides questions to help you apply the truth from your weekly Nourish Scripture. **Sometimes you may not have answers for all six questions.**

IMAGE OF GOD TO TRUST? An attribute of God, Jesus, or the Holy Spirit to trust.

MESSAGE TO SHARE? A word of encouragement, truth, or prayer to share.

PROMISE TO TREASURE? A promise in the Bible to believe.

ACTION TO TAKE? A specific step God is calling you to take.

CORE IDENTITY IN CHRIST TO AFFIRM? A truth about how God sees you to affirm.

TRANSGRESSION TO CONFESS? A sin to acknowledge for help, healing, and restoration through Christ.

3 AFFIRM YOUR IDENTITY IN CHRIST.

Conclude your quiet time by turning to the AFFIRMATION section on page 97 to read your "In Christ, I Am" statements aloud.

DAY FOUR > RENEW

Nourish Scripture: _____

1 PRAY.

Pray with purpose following the framework on your Weekly Personal Prayer Sheet.

2 TAKE THE *RENEW* STEP OF THE NOURISH™ BIBLE STUDY METHOD.

Like an anchor that secures its vessel, biblical meditation secures truth to transform your life. Take five minutes to *renew* your mind by focusing on one word, verse, or truth that the Holy Spirit revealed through the Bible during your week of study. Record your truth below and on your Anchor of Truth card. Quiet your thoughts. Focus on the truth. Read the truth. Pray the truth.

My anchor of truth

3 RECORD AND REVIEW ATTRIBUTES OF GOD.

Write the attributes you discovered from yesterday's IMPACT question "An Image of God to Trust" in the GOD IS section on page 111.

4 DEFINE AND DECLARE WHO YOU ARE IN CHRIST.

Reflect on your answers to yesterday's IMPACT question "A Core Identity in Christ to Affirm." Rewrite one answer as an "In Christ, I Am" statement in the AFFIRMATION section on page 97 and read aloud.

DAY FIVE > CONNECT

1 PRAY.

Pray with purpose following the framework on your Weekly Personal Prayer Sheet.

2 CONNECT AND SHARE TRUTH.

Watch the weekly teaching message called the Treasured Tribe Talk and consider posting your thoughts online. To discover more, visit www.TreasuredMinistries.com/devotions.

MY NOTES
Rest and Reflect

The remaining days in your week provide time to rest, reflect, and catch up on any days of study you may have missed during the week. Use the space below however you decide. You could take notes from your small group time if applicable, write down additional thoughts from your week of study, record sermon notes, journal, list your goals and dreams, or just leave these pages blank. It's entirely up to you!

AFFIRMATION

"This means that anyone who
belongs to Christ has become a new person.
The old life is gone; a new life has begun!"

—2 Corinthians 5:17

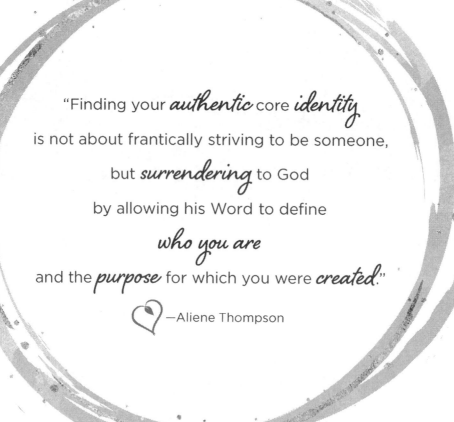

"Finding your *authentic* core *identity*

is not about frantically striving to be someone,

but *surrendering* to God

by allowing his Word to define

who you are

and the *purpose* for which you were *created*."

—Aliene Thompson

AFFIRMATION

Who I Am in Christ

AFFIRM YOUR AUTHENTIC IDENTITY > DECLARE GOD'S TRUTH

Rewrite your answers from the IMPACT™ question on your Nourish™ Notes "A Core Identity in Christ to Affirm" in an "In Christ, I am" statement. See below for examples.

In Christ, I am ...

I am God's child. (John 1:12)

I am completely forgiven. (Romans 3:21–22)

I am listening to the Lord because his words bring life. (John 6:68)

I am very valuable to God. (Matthew 10:31)

I am bringing my needs to God in prayer because he cares and wants me
to do just that. (Luke 11:9–13)

I am not aiming for perfection. I am pursuing Jesus instead.
(Philippians 3:3–10)

I am confident in asking God for wisdom. (Jeremiah 33:2–3)

AFFIRMATION

Who I Am in Christ

AFFIRM YOUR AUTHENTIC IDENTITY > DECLARE GOD'S TRUTH

Rewrite your answers from the IMPACT question on your Nourish Notes "A Core Identity in Christ to Affirm" in an "In Christ, I Am" statement.

In Christ, I am . . .

AFFIRMATION

Who I Am in Christ

AFFIRM YOUR AUTHENTIC IDENTITY > DECLARE GOD'S TRUTH

Rewrite your answers from the IMPACT question on your Nourish Notes "A Core Identity in Christ to Affirm" in an "In Christ, I Am" statement.

In Christ, I am . . .

_____

_____

_____

_____

_____

_____

_____

_____

_____

_____

_____

_____

_____

_____

_____

_____

_____

AFFIRMATION

Who I Am in Christ

AFFIRM YOUR AUTHENTIC IDENTITY > DECLARE GOD'S TRUTH

Rewrite your answers from the IMPACT question on your Nourish Notes "A Core Identity in Christ to Affirm" in an "In Christ, I Am" statement.

In Christ, I am . . .

AFFIRMATION

Who I Am in Christ

AFFIRM YOUR AUTHENTIC IDENTITY > DECLARE GOD'S TRUTH

Rewrite your answers from the IMPACT question on your Nourish Notes "A Core Identity in Christ to Affirm" in an "In Christ, I Am" statement.

In Christ, I am . . .

AFFIRMATION

Who I Am in Christ

AFFIRM YOUR AUTHENTIC IDENTITY > DECLARE GOD'S TRUTH

Rewrite your answers from the IMPACT question on your Nourish Notes "A Core Identity in Christ to Affirm" in an "In Christ, I Am" statement.

In Christ, I am . . .

AFFIRMATION

Who I Am in Christ

AFFIRM YOUR AUTHENTIC IDENTITY > DECLARE GOD'S TRUTH

Rewrite your answers from the IMPACT question on your Nourish Notes "A Core Identity in Christ to Affirm" in an "In Christ, I Am" statement.

In Christ, I am . . .

_____

_____

_____

_____

_____

_____

_____

_____

_____

_____

_____

_____

_____

_____

_____

_____

_____

_____

_____

AFFIRMATION

Who I Am in Christ

AFFIRM YOUR AUTHENTIC IDENTITY > DECLARE GOD'S TRUTH

Rewrite your answers from the IMPACT question on your Nourish Notes "A Core Identity in Christ to Affirm" in an "In Christ, I Am" statement.

In Christ, I am . . .

AFFIRMATION

Who I Am in Christ

AFFIRM YOUR AUTHENTIC IDENTITY > DECLARE GOD'S TRUTH

Rewrite your answers from the IMPACT question on your Nourish Notes "A Core Identity in Christ to Affirm" in an "In Christ, I Am" statement.

In Christ, I am . . .

AFFIRMATION

Who I Am in Christ

AFFIRM YOUR AUTHENTIC IDENTITY > DECLARE GOD'S TRUTH

Rewrite your answers from the IMPACT question on your Nourish Notes "A Core Identity in Christ to Affirm" in an "In Christ, I Am" statement.

In Christ, I am . . .

AFFIRMATION

Who I Am in Christ

AFFIRM YOUR AUTHENTIC IDENTITY > DECLARE GOD'S TRUTH

Rewrite your answers from the IMPACT question on your Nourish Notes "A Core Identity in Christ to Affirm" in an "In Christ, I Am" statement.

In Christ, I am . . .

AFFIRMATION

Who I Am in Christ

AFFIRM YOUR AUTHENTIC IDENTITY > DECLARE GOD'S TRUTH

Rewrite your answers from the IMPACT question on your Nourish Notes "A Core Identity in Christ to Affirm" in an "In Christ, I Am" statement.

In Christ, I am . . .

_____

_____

_____

_____

_____

_____

_____

_____

_____

_____

_____

_____

_____

_____

_____

_____

_____

GOD IS

"I also pray that you will understand
the incredible greatness of God's power
for us who believe him."

—*Ephesians 1:19*

"*Christianity that requires courage*
instead of Christianity that demands comfort
calls us to stand in the strength
that only God can provide."

—Aliene Thompson

GOD IS

Attributes of God, Jesus, or the Holy Spirit

BUILD YOUR LIST > BUILD YOUR FAITH

Use this space to write down the attributes you discovered from the IMPACT™ question on your Nourish™ Notes "An Image of God to Trust." We provided a list to get you started.

The Maker of Heaven and Earth (Jeremiah 33:2)

Restores (Jeremiah 33:7)

Lord of the Heaven's Armies (Jeremiah 33:11)

Healer (Mark 2:11)

Counselor (John 14:25)

GOD IS

Attributes of God, Jesus, or the Holy Spirit

BUILD YOUR LIST > BUILD YOUR FAITH

Use this space to write down the attributes you discovered from the IMPACT question on your Nourish Notes "An Image of God to Trust."

GOD IS

Attributes of God, Jesus, or the Holy Spirit

BUILD YOUR LIST > BUILD YOUR FAITH

Use this space to write down the attributes you discovered from the IMPACT question on your Nourish Notes "An Image of God to Trust."

GOD IS

Attributes of God, Jesus, or the Holy Spirit

BUILD YOUR LIST > BUILD YOUR FAITH

Use this space to write down the attributes you discovered from the IMPACT question on your Nourish Notes "An Image of God to Trust."

GOD IS

Attributes of God, Jesus, or the Holy Spirit

BUILD YOUR LIST > BUILD YOUR FAITH

Use this space to write down the attributes you discovered from the IMPACT question on your Nourish Notes "An Image of God to Trust."

GOD IS

Attributes of God, Jesus, or the Holy Spirit

BUILD YOUR LIST > BUILD YOUR FAITH

Use this space to write down the attributes you discovered from the IMPACT question on your Nourish Notes "An Image of God to Trust."

GOD IS

Attributes of God, Jesus, or the Holy Spirit

BUILD YOUR LIST > BUILD YOUR FAITH

Use this space to write down the attributes you discovered from the IMPACT question on your Nourish Notes "An Image of God to Trust."

GOD IS

Attributes of God, Jesus, or the Holy Spirit

BUILD YOUR LIST > BUILD YOUR FAITH

Use this space to write down the attributes you discovered from the IMPACT question on your Nourish Notes "An Image of God to Trust."

GOD IS

Attributes of God, Jesus, or the Holy Spirit

BUILD YOUR LIST > BUILD YOUR FAITH

Use this space to write down the attributes you discovered from the IMPACT question on your Nourish Notes "An Image of God to Trust."

GOD IS

Attributes of God, Jesus, or the Holy Spirit

BUILD YOUR LIST > BUILD YOUR FAITH

Use this space to write down the attributes you discovered from the IMPACT question on your Nourish Notes "An Image of God to Trust."

GOD IS

Attributes of God, Jesus, or the Holy Spirit

BUILD YOUR LIST > BUILD YOUR FAITH

Use this space to write down the attributes you discovered from the IMPACT question on your Nourish Notes "An Image of God to Trust."

GOD IS

Attributes of God, Jesus, or the Holy Spirit

BUILD YOUR LIST > BUILD YOUR FAITH

Use this space to write down the attributes you discovered from the IMPACT question on your Nourish Notes "An Image of God to Trust."

MY SPACE

"My heart has heard you say,
'Come and talk with me.'
And my heart responds,
'LORD, I am coming.'"

—*Psalm 27:8*

"*Worship* intercepts
insecurity."

—Aliene Thompson

The ***Nourish™ Notebook*** binder starter kit is as unique as your purpose. We want it to be tailored to fit your needs, so we made it customizable. You can add the pages you need for your journey. The features include:

- Embossed vegan leather 1-inch binder available in Slate, Fawn, or Cocoa.

- 17 weeks of Nourish Note pages to record all that God says to you as you spend time in his Word.

- Tabbed dividers for quick access to each section.

- Snap-in Nourish bookmark to hold your position in the binder.

- Includes a set of Anchor of Truth Cards.

- Heavy weight, smooth writing paper.

- Downloadable calendar to print included.

- Refill pages available.

- Proudly printed and designed in the USA.

To purchase your copy, visit: **www.TreasuredMinistries.com/shop**

Made in the USA
Columbia, SC
02 October 2021